Contents

The big match
Focus on: ar, or as in *farm, for* 3

Snapshots
Focus on: er as in *her* 9

The bird girls
Focus on: ir as in *girl* 15

My very bad morning
Focus on: ur, wr as in *fur, write* 23

Phonemes: ch, sh, th, wh, ph, a_e, ai, ay, e_e, ea, ee, y *as e*, i_e, ie, igh, y *as i*, o_e, oa, ow, u_e, ue, oo, ew, ar, or, er, ir, ur, wr

'Tricky' words: my, can't, does, love, here, are, look, our, eyes, house, were

About this book

These short stories are designed to give children blending and reading practice. They are decodable, which means the words in them only include letter shapes and sounds that the children have learned. The stories gradually introduce 'tricky' words, building on the learning in the Red Series.

The progression links directly to the teaching order in the Letterland teaching range. Each story begins with a title page that provides important information for children and teachers.

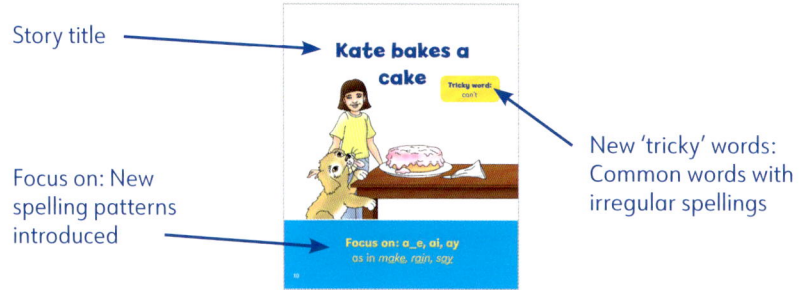

Story title

Focus on: New spelling patterns introduced

New 'tricky' words: Common words with irregular spellings

Basic teaching tips:

- Encourage the sounding out of decodable words (and any decodable parts of 'tricky' words).
- Discuss the stories with the children to ensure comprehension and engagement.
- Encourage re-reading in pairs or individually to develop fluency and reading for meaning.

Red Series introduces the a-z letters and sounds and some 'tricky words'. On completion of this series, the following words remain tricky in part: **a, the, she, oh, for, that, ok, they, says, her, this, to, said, of, what, you, was, want, come, sees, asks, do.** These words are included in **Blue Series**.

The big match

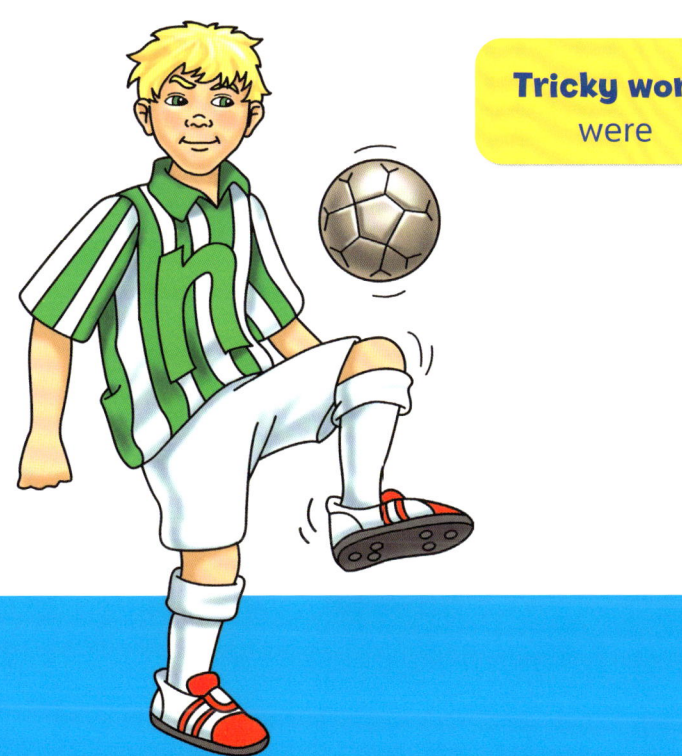

Tricky word:
were

Focus on: ar, or
as in <u>far</u>m, <u>for</u>

It was the morning of a big match for Nick's team. Nick put on his shorts and started playing in the yard.

Then Mum said, "Nick, can you go to the store for me? I need parsnips and sweetcorn."

"But Mum, I have a big match today!" Nick cried.

"It's not far. The more you do, the more you *can* do!" said Mum.

The store was on the north shore. He got the sweetcorn and parsnips.

When Nick got home Dad said, "Nick, I need you to do a few chores."

"But Dad, I have a big match today!" Nick cried.

"The chores are not hard. The more you do, the more you *can* do!" said Dad.

Nick helped to clean the car, then swept the porch and the storm drain. But he kept on kicking, too.

Then Dad beeped the horn on the car. "Get in!" he said. "It's time for the big match!"

The match started and Nick played hard. The score was tied. A lot of the team was worn out, but not Nick. He scored the winning goal.

"The more you do, the more you *can* do!" said Nick, as he smiled at Mum and Dad.

Snapshots

Focus on: er as in *h<u>er</u>*

This is my sister, Jennifer. She is a swimmer.

This summer she got this silver cup. She says she will be an even better swimmer by next summer.

This is Peter. He is bigger and older than me.

Peter is a reader. His teacher says he is clever and a quicker reader than her!

This is Oliver. He is tiny and he is a biter. My mum says he is teething.

I tell him he must never, ever bite me. But I don't think he understands 'never' or 'ever'.

This is Sniffer. She likes to smell things. She even likes to smell my feet!

When it gets hotter in the summer she drinks lots and jumps in pools. She is a swimmer, too.

This is me. My mum says I am a thinker. I think of what I will be when I get older.

I am fit so I might be a runner, a tennis player or a golfer. Or... maybe I will be a writer!

The bird girls

Focus on: ir as in *gi<u>r</u>l*

Twirly Bird and Swirly Bird were in the nest. The twins were getting dressed for a birthday party.

"I am going to put on my red shirt," chirped Twirly Bird.

Twirly bird looked at her shirt. "Oh, no, this shirt is dirty," she cried. "What can I put on for the birthday party?"

Swirly Bird said "I'll put on my pink skirt."

Swirly looked down. "Oh, no, no! I forgot. I squirted blue paint on it in art class. What are we going to do?"

Just then Mummy Bird came flying up to the nest.

"Mum, we don't have a thing to put on for the birthday party!" cried Swirly. "My skirt is dirty."

"And my red shirt is dirty," sobbed Twirly.

"Girls, girls, you don't need a shirt or a skirt," Mum tweeted.

"Don't we?" peeped both girls.

"You are red and green and blue. You look perfect just as you are!" said Mummy Bird.

"Do you think so?" asked Swirly.

"Perfect," Mum chirped.

"We look perfect?" asked Twirly.

"Perfect!" she chirped firmly for the third time.

Then Twirly twirled up into the sky. She sang, "I am perfect. You are perfect. Let's go to the birthday party!"

"Wait for me, Twirly!" Swirly swirled into the sky with her twin.

My very bad morning

Focus on: ur, wr
as in *f<u>ur</u>*, *<u>wr</u>ite*

It was Thursday morning but my alarm clock did not wake me up.

My cat, Furry woke me up. She has long, thick fur.

She was on my chest, purring. Her long, thick fur made me sneeze... three times!

I looked at the clock in a blur.

Oh, no! I was going to be late for the bus!

I got up and hurled Furry down onto the rug.
She screamed and ran to the door. It was closed.

I wrenched the door lever and it fell off!

My dog, Curly, started to bark. Her fur is curly. Dad came to see why Curly was barking. He pulled the door and it burst open.

I fell into the kitchen. I was thirsty and needed a drink. I tripped on Curly who was lurking on her mat. I hurt my wrist on a fork.

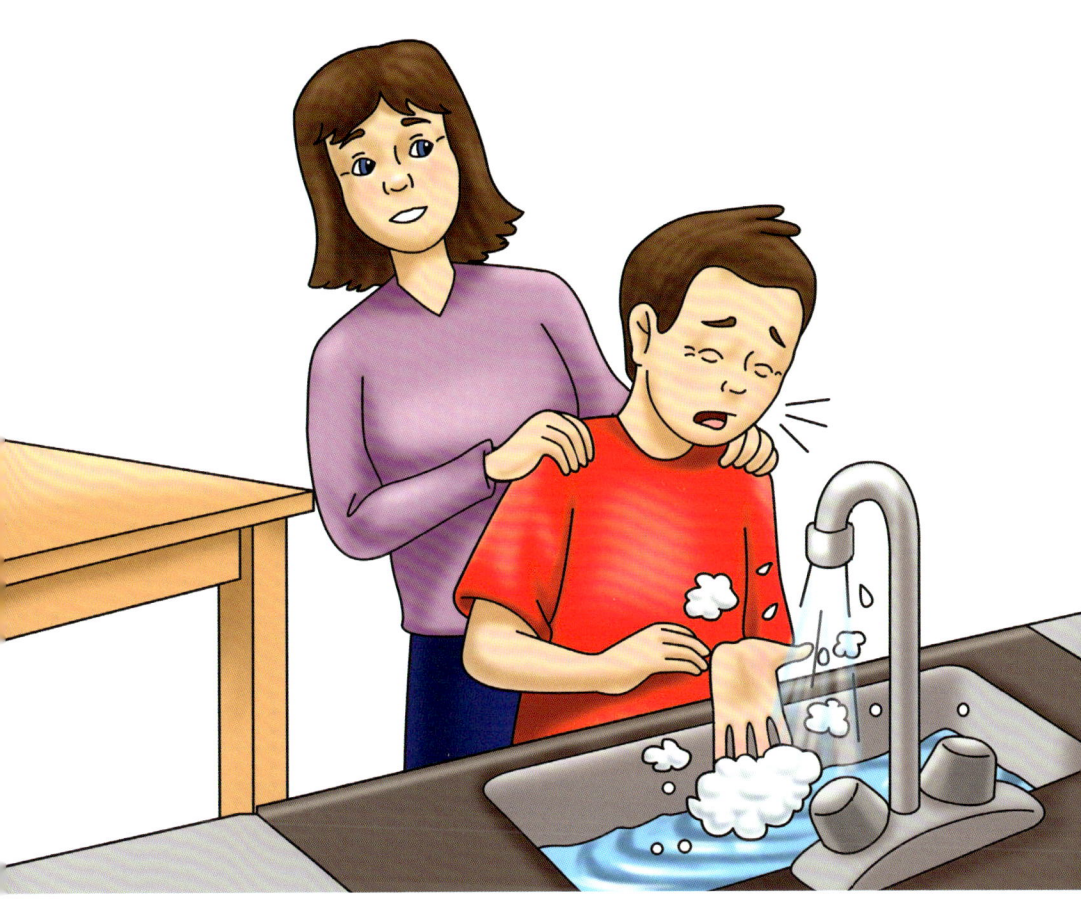

I tried to put it under the cold tap, but I turned on the wrong tap and I got a hot spurt! It burned my hand.

Mum came in and said, "Let me see that!"

"No, Mum, I will be late for the bus."

"Bus? There are no classes today.
It's Saturday!" said Mum.
So it was *not* a Thursday!
Just a very bad morning!

About this series

This series of 10 books accompanies the Letterland teaching range. Each book contains a selection of short stories. In total there are 32 engaging stories featuring the phonic elements listed below as well as some 'tricky' high-frequency words.

Book	Focus elements	As in the word...	Story titles
1	sh, ch, th, th, wh, ph	chip, shop, that, thing	Check on the chicks Shep and me What is that thing?
2	a_e, ai, ay	make, rain, say,	A safe place Kate bakes a cake Kane's tail!
3	e_e, ea, ee, y	these, sea, bee, baby	A trip to the sea Mr E's trees Happy!
4	i_e, ie, igh, y	like, tie, night, my	Ben rides his bike Cats at night What a mess!
5	o_e, oa, ow	home, boat, show	The bad goat When the cold wind blows Lost in the Queen's maze
6	u_e, ue, oo, ew	cube, blue, moon, few, grew	Stuck on a dune A day at the zoo The Hat Man's new roof
7	ar, or, er, ir, ur, wr	farm, for, her, girl, fur, write	The big match Snapshots The bird girls My very bad morning
8	o, oo, u, oy, oi	son, book, put, boy, coin	Oscar's brother The big pull Nick's noisy new toy
9	aw, au, ow, ou	saw, cause, how, out,	Draw it! The house mouse Look now!
10	Review ear, air	pear, year, fair	My shark dream A fresh feast Bears at the fair A fairy story

Collect the sets

Phonics Readers - Red Series

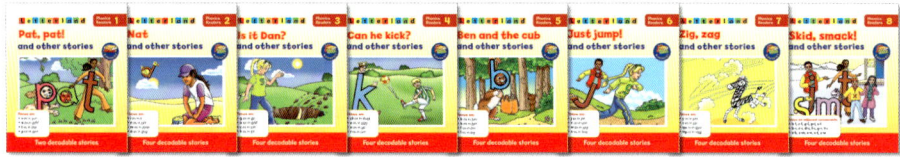

Phonics Readers - Blue Series

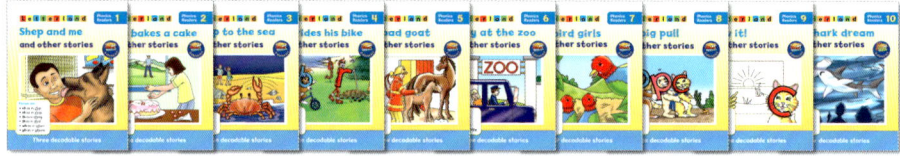

Published by Letterland International Ltd. 8/10 South Street, Epsom, Surrey, KT18 7PF, UK.
www.letterland.com
ISBN: 978-1-78248-186-7
Product Code: TJ08

© Letterland International 2016
LETTERLAND™ is a trademark of Letterland International Ltd.

First published 2013. This new edition published 2016.
Reprinted 2023.
10 9 8 7 6 5 4 3 2

Authors: Stamey Carter and Lisa Holt
Originator of Letterland: Lyn Wendon
Artwork: Baz Rowell
Design: Lisa Holt

The author asserts the moral right to be identified as the author of this work. All rights reserved. No part of this publication may be reproduced, stored in a retrieval system, or transmitted in any form or by any means, electronic, mechanical, photocopying, recording or otherwise, without either the prior permission of the Publisher or a licence permitting restricted copying in the United Kingdom issued by the Copyright Licensing Agency Ltd, 90 Tottenham Court Road, London W1T 4LP. This book is sold subject to the condition that it shall not be by way of trade or otherwise be lent, hired out or otherwise circulated without the Publisher's prior consent.

Printed in Beirut, Lebanon.